Enjoyable English

Glenys O'Connell

Wizard Whimstaff lives in a faraway land, in a magical cave. He searches for apprentices so he can pass on his powerful English spells. And this time Wizard Whimstaff has chosen you!

He has a goblin helper called Pointy, who is very clever. Pointy helps Wizard Whimstaff keep his spell books tidy. He also stirs the smelly cauldron to make words appear.

Pointy has two pet frogs called Mugly and Bugly. They are very lazy. They spend most of their time eating, burping and sleeping. Their friend Miss Snufflebeam also lives in the cave. She is a small dragon. She cannot breathe fire yet, so puffs little clouds of smoke instead!

Wizard Whimstaff and his friends are very happy, solving English problems. Join them on a magical quest to win the Trophy of English Wizardry!

Contents

Creepy Capitals

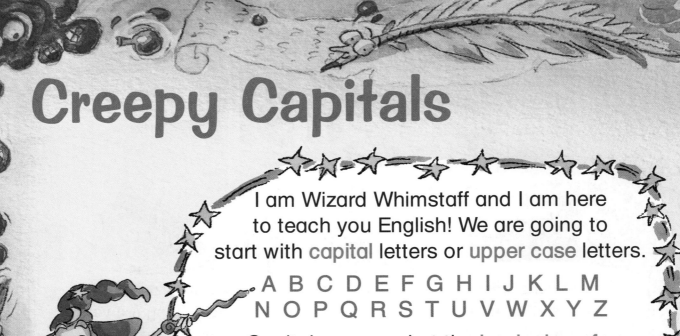

I am Wizard Whimstaff and I am here to teach you English! We are going to start with capital letters or upper case letters.

A B C D E F G H I J K L M
N O P Q R S T U V W X Y Z

Capitals are used at the beginning of a sentence and for proper names.

I am going to London.

Full stops are the dots at the end of a sentence. They show that a sentence has finished.

The dragon chased the cat.

Task 1 Look at the sentences below. At the beginning of each one is both a capital and a small letter. Can you put a circle around the letter that should start the sentence?

a T t he fat frog fell off his lily pad.

b w W hen are we going to have tea?

c M m y Mother has gone to the shops.

d T t oday is my birthday.

e w W here is my wand?

f i l t is very sunny outside.

g W w e like the summer holidays!

Task 2 Wave your magic wand and circle the words below that should have a capital letter.

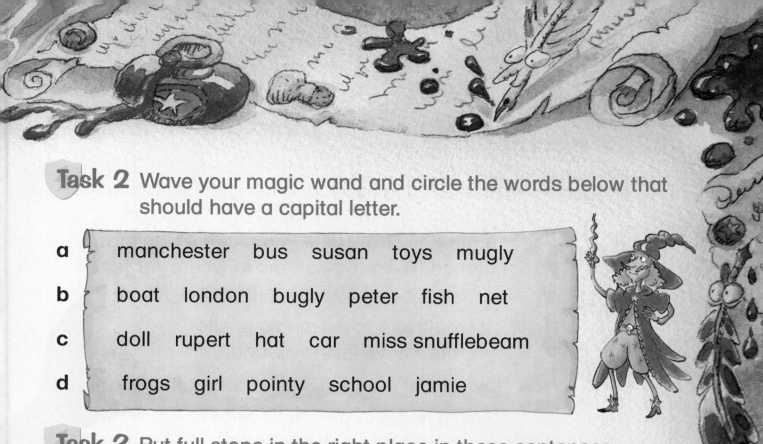

a manchester   bus   susan   toys   mugly

b boat   london   bugly   peter   fish   net

c doll   rupert   hat   car   miss snufflebeam

d frogs   girl   pointy   school   jamie

Task 3 Put full stops in the right place in these sentences. Allakazan!

a The frog is hopping

b That is Miss Snufflebeam's ball

c We are going to the shops

d It is time for school

e My daddy is going to work

f Mugly and Bugly are snoozing

g Pointy is very clever

h Let's go to bed

Sorcerer's Skill Check

Now use your magic to put a line under the letters that should be capital letters in these sentences. Then put in the full stops. Hey presto!

a sari and paul are going to school

b we are going to visit the seaside at blackpool

c i wish it was the summer holidays

Super! Collect your first silver shield and stick it on the trophy at the back of the book!

3

Croaky Commas

I am Miss Snufflebeam and I get very confused about grammar! I have to talk to you about commas. They help you make sense of a sentence. We put a comma in where we take a breath. Read this sentence out loud:

I would like to do magic spells
but I have lost my wand.

Now read it out loud with a comma:

I would like to do magic spells,
but I have lost my wand.

See how much easier that is?

Task 1 Please help me put commas in these sentences.

a Mugly likes to eat cheese but Bugly likes sweets better.

b We are going to school so why don't you walk with us?

c I left my wand on the table but now I can't find it.

Task 2 Commas can also help us to separate lists. Will you put the commas in these sentences for me? Wizard Whimstaff has done the first one for us.

a It is time for Peter, Susan and Sean to go home.

b Miss Snufflebeam Pointy and Wizard Whimstaff live in a cave.

c Where are the sandwiches cakes and drinks?

d I like to play football tennis and tag.

Task 3 Sometimes two commas are used to show who is being spoken to. Help me to put commas in these sentences. I have done the first one.

a I wanted to say, Jimmy, that you are doing well in school.

b Listen to me class I want you all to come to the library.

c Are we going to the cave Pointy or to my house?

d What time Jamal do you have to be home?

e I am sorry Miss Brown that I am late.

f Read this book the teacher said then we will have a test.

g Excuse me boys and girls dinner is ready.

Sorcerer's Skill Check

I am a bit confused! Can you put commas in the right places in these sentences?

a I wanted to play but I had to go to Grandma's house.

b My teacher Miss Snufflebeam is a dragon.

c Wizard Whimstaff are you ready to make some magic?

d John Peter and I are going to Jamal's house.

e Put your coat on Ann it is time to go.

Burp! You have another silver shield for your trophy!

Amazing Alphabet

I am Pointy, Wizard Whimstaff's assistant. Alphabetical ordering is a way of putting words in the right order. Here are the letters of the alphabet in the right order:

a b c d e f g h i j k l m n o p q r s t u v w x y z

You sort words by the order of their first letters. The letter c comes before d in the alphabet. So a word starting with c goes before a word starting with d.

cat   dog   elf   frog

You will soon get the hang of it!

Task 1 These letters are in alphabetical order but some are missing! Can you complete the empty bricks?

a d e ☐ g h   d m n ☐ p

b j k l ☐ n   e r s ☐ u

c g ☐ i j k   f w ☐ y ☐

Task 2 Super! Put these words in alphabetical order by writing them on the lines. If you look at the alphabet, you can see that **bat** would come first!

a _____

b _____

c _____

d _____

cat

house

bat

dragon

Task 3 Practice makes perfect! Here are some more words to put in alphabetical order, just like the last exercise. Use the alphabet on page six to help you.

a _____

b _____

c _____

d _____

e _____

f _____

g _____

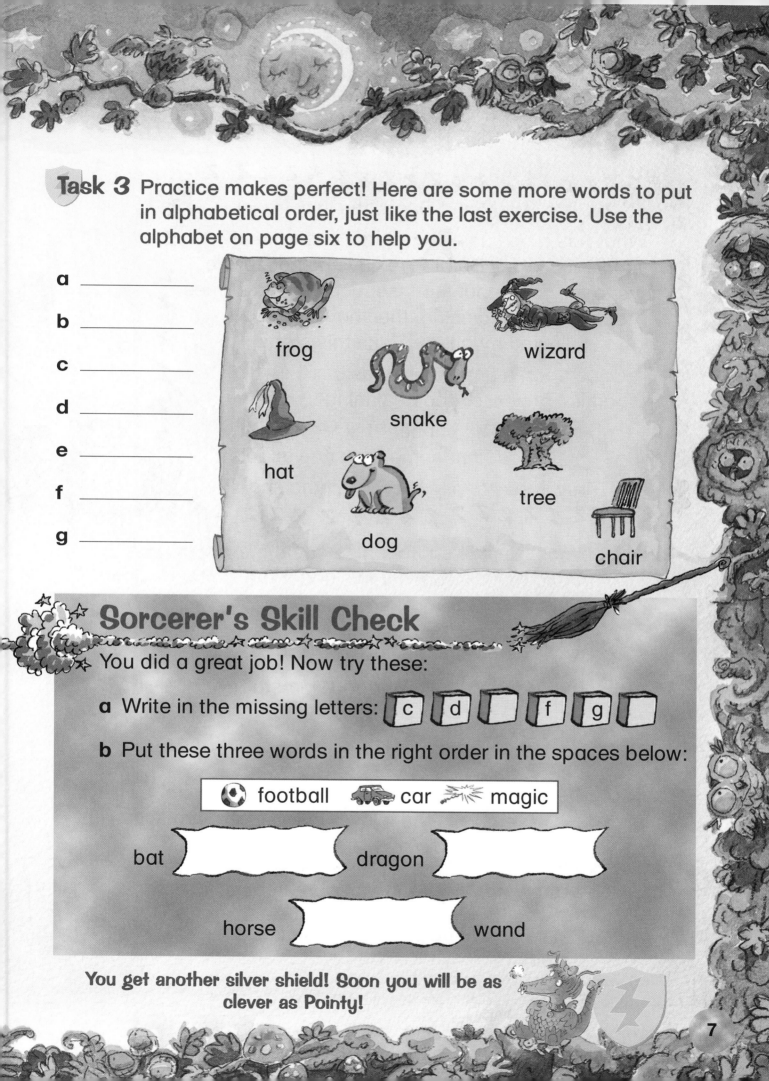

frog

wizard

snake

hat

tree

dog

chair

Sorcerer's Skill Check

You did a great job! Now try these:

a Write in the missing letters: c d ☐ f g ☐

b Put these three words in the right order in the spaces below:

⚽ football   🚗 car   💥 magic

bat _____   dragon _____

horse _____   wand

You get another silver shield! Soon you will be as clever as Pointy!

Super Sequencing

We are Mugly and Bugly, the lazy frogs!

What has a beginning, a middle and an end? A story, of course! Before we have a snooze, we have to tell you about story sequencing. All stories start with a beginning, then have a middle, followed by an end. Like this story:

Once upon a time, there was a beautiful princess. (the beginning)

The princess fell in love with a handsome frog. (the middle)

They lived happily ever after. (the end)

Task 1 Croak! Here is another nice frog story. Wave your magic wand to draw a line under the sentence that starts the story.

Mugly and Bugly are two handsome green frogs.

They worked all day to help Wizard Whimstaff.

Then they had a long snooze.

Task 2 The next part should be the middle of the story. Like a lunch break is in the middle of the day! Burp! Can you choose the middle of this story?

Mugly and Bugly are two handsome green frogs.

They worked all day to help Wizard Whimstaff.

Then they had a long snooze.

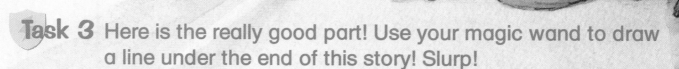

Task 3 Here is the really good part! Use your magic wand to draw a line under the end of this story! Slurp!

Mugly and Bugly are two handsome green frogs.

They worked all day to help Wizard Whimstaff.

Then they had a long snooze.

Sorcerer's Skill Check

We need to have a snooze now. These stories are mixed up. Can you draw a line under the sentence that you think begins each of these stories?

a He got first prize.

John can run very fast.

He entered a race at school.

b She scores a lot of goals.

Now she is on the school team.

Emma likes to play football.

c We saw lions and tigers.

Now we are tired.

We went to the zoo.

Well done, young apprentice! Add another silver shield to your trophy!

9

Revolting Rhyme

Hello, young apprentice!
I love words that rhyme!

My wizard's <u>cat</u>
Sleeps on the <u>mat</u>.
You can see <u>that</u>
He is very <u>fat</u>.

See, cat, mat, that and fat
are all words that sound alike.
Hey presto! They rhyme!

Task 1 Draw a line to join each of these rhyming words! Just do the best you can!

a (frog)   **b** (fox)   **c** (lock)   **d** (king)   **e** (bat)   **f** (hay)

(rock)   (sing)   (box)   (dog)   (say)   (cat)

Task 2 These words sound like the ones in the questions below. Put them in the right places. Do not worry if it seems hard at first!

dog	sing	tag	rose	fox	hat

a king ring [___]   **d** bat cat [___]

b box pox [___]   **e** rag bag [___]

c log frog [___]   **f** hose nose [___]

Task 3 I knew you could do it! Now, wave your magic wand and circle the words that don't rhyme.

a frog   dog   log   (pig)   **e** pat   rat   cat   dog

b fox   sing   king   ring   **f** din   bin   apple   chin

c rock   lock   dragon   clock   **g** purple   sat   rat   cat

d see   wizard   tea   bee   **h** map   lap   hat   tap

Sorcerer's Skill Check

Allakazan! Complete these exercises to become a rhyme wizard!

First draw lines to join the words that rhyme.

a sing   **b** new   **c** cat   **d** log

blew   ring   dog   hat

Now choose a word from the box to rhyme with a word below.

cool   see   pin   pat

e sat   **f** tool

g bee   **h** tin

Take another silver shield while we take a snooze!

Cool Consonants

Consonants are special letters.
I think consonants are all the letters that are not vowels. Vowels are soft-sounding. Most of the time, consonants sound hard.

Wizard Whimstaff says that the vowels are a e i o u which means that the letters b c d f g h j k l m n p q r s t v w x y z are consonants.

Look at the word top. It starts with a consonant and ends with a consonant, with the vowel o in the middle.

Task 1 Help! Draw a magic circle around the words that start with a consonant. I have done the first one to show you how!

a (man) apple (dog) out   d ask (wizard) (frog) (wand) in

b (jam) (zoo) (pot) ant (yes)   e (bee) ant elephant (flower)

c (bat) (pip) (ring) on (pan)   f all (game) (king) (pin) elf

Task 2 I am confused! Put the consonant letters **p** and **t** in front of these words and read the new word out loud to me.

p

a p_ant   b t_an   c p_in   d t_en   e p_ig

f t_ip   g t_ap   h p_all   i t_in   j p_en

t

Task 3 I am still confused! Can you make some new words with the letter in the comet?

s

a ___at   b ___plat   c ___mile   d ___lip

b

e ___at   f ___et   g ___all   h ___urp

w

i ___all   j ___et   k ___ail   l ___ell   m ___as

g

n ___et   o ___row   p ___rey   q ___randma

Sorcerer's Skill Check

a Draw a circle around the word that does not begin with a consonant.

    can fish
    egg tree

b Draw a circle around all the words here that end with a consonant.

    pin cat hello
    wand zoo

c Draw a circle around all the words that start **and** end with a consonant.

    pat one kid
    doll blue

Excellent work, young apprentice! You can put another silver shield on your trophy!

Apprentice Wizard Challenge 1

Challenge 1 Put a circle around the letter that should start the sentence.

a (G g) o to school.

b (w W) here is Pointy?

c (c C) an we go to the zoo?

d (W w) e will go in the summer holidays.

e (M m) ugly and Bugly are two greedy frogs.

f (t T) he postman brought us a letter.

Challenge 2 Put commas in these sentences.

a I would like to do magic spells but I have lost my wand.

b It is time for Mugly Bugly and Miss Snufflebeam to go home.

c We like to play football tennis and skipping.

d Are we going shopping Mummy or are we going to Grandma's?

e Wizard Whimstaff where is your wand?

Challenge 3 Put these words in the right order in the bottles below.

dragon   fish   wizard

car    elf    Pointy

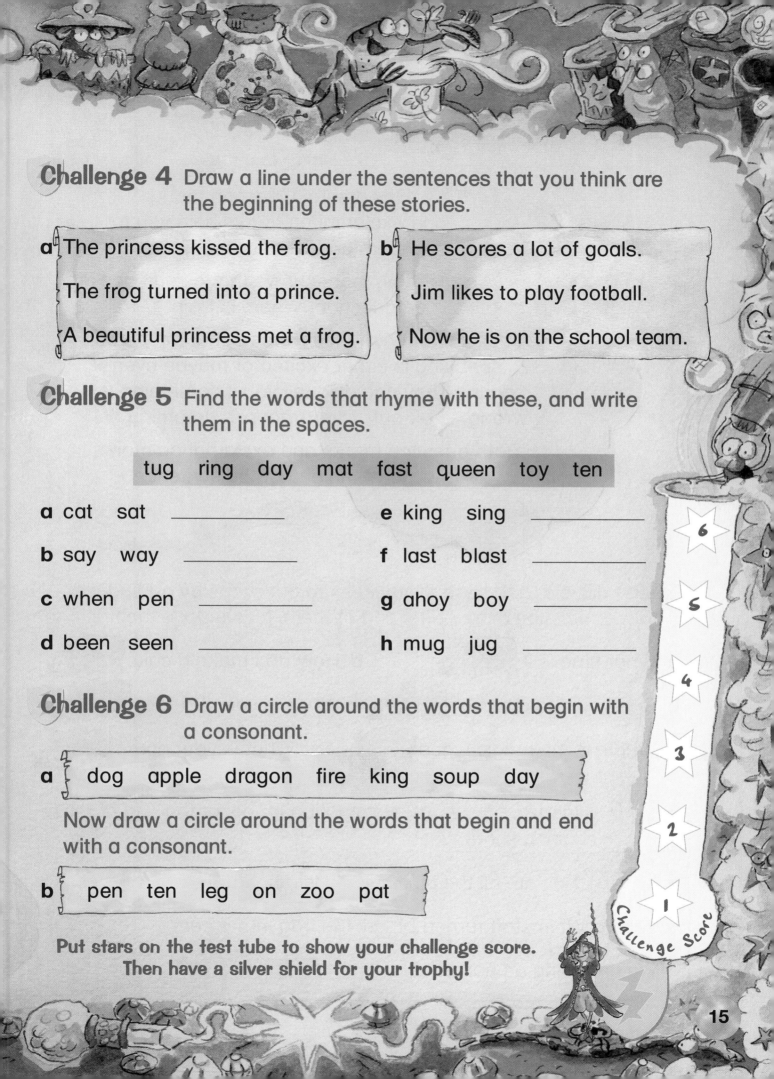

Challenge 4 Draw a line under the sentences that you think are the beginning of these stories.

a The princess kissed the frog.

The frog turned into a prince.

A beautiful princess met a frog.

b He scores a lot of goals.

Jim likes to play football.

Now he is on the school team.

Challenge 5 Find the words that rhyme with these, and write them in the spaces.

| tug | ring | day | mat | fast | queen | toy | ten |

a cat   sat   _____

b say   way   _____

c when   pen   _____

d been   seen   _____

e king   sing   _____

f last   blast   _____

g ahoy   boy   _____

h mug   jug   _____

Challenge 6 Draw a circle around the words that begin with a consonant.

a   dog   apple   dragon   fire   king   soup   day

Now draw a circle around the words that begin and end with a consonant.

b   pen   ten   leg   on   zoo   pat

Put stars on the test tube to show your challenge score.
Then have a silver shield for your trophy!

6

5

4

3

2

1

Challenge Score

Messy Marks

Hey presto! Question marks and exclamation marks help you to understand what is being said.

A question mark shows that a sentence is a question. Where is Pointy?

An exclamation mark shows us that the person speaking is either excited or maybe even angry! They can also tell you if something is wrong. Look out! That dragon is breathing fire!

Both question marks and exclamation marks always go at the end of the sentence.

Task 1 Show that these sentences are questions by putting a question mark at the end of them. I have done the first one.

a What time is it **?**

b Can you ride a bicycle

c Where is my magic wand

d How do I make a cake

e When is your birthday

f What is your name

Task 2 Allakazan! Now put exclamation marks at the end of these exciting sentences!

a My dog Rex ate all the biscuits. He is a bad dog____

b Wizard Whimstaff turned Mugly the frog into a cat____

c We are going on holiday____

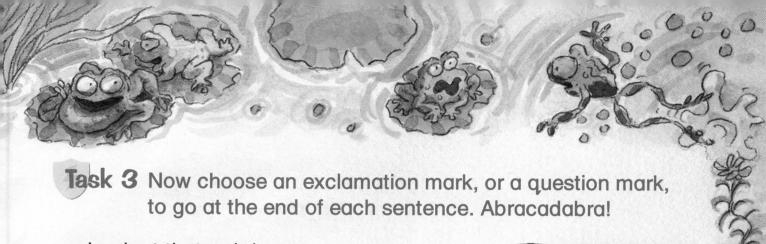

Task 3 Now choose an exclamation mark, or a question mark, to go at the end of each sentence. Abracadabra!

a Look at that red dragon____

b Do you like sweets____

c When do the school holidays start____

d That house is on fire____

e Do you like to read____

f Yes, I love to read____

g Question marks and exclamation marks are fun____

h Will Wizard Whimstaff be there____

Sorcerer's Skill Check

Work your magic and put question marks or exclamation marks in the stars.

   a Are Mugly and Bugly asleep

   b Peter scored a goal

   c Watch out   Don't drop that glass

   d Is it time for tea

   e We are all going to Pointy's birthday party

You soon got the hang of it! Now get another silver shield!

Magic oo and ee

Burp! Some letters say more when you put them together! For example, when you put the letter o with another letter o, you have the sound oo, like in m<u>oo</u>n or sp<u>oo</u>n or ball<u>oo</u>n.

When you put e and e together, they make a sound like in tr<u>ee</u> or thr<u>ee</u> or s<u>ee</u>.

Task 1 Put the letters **oo** into the spaces to find out what these words are. We are going for a sn**oo**ze while you are busy!

a m___n   br___m   b___t   **d** t___t   h___t   l___t

b ball___n   z___   f___d   **e** m___   c___t___

c c___l   sch___l   p___l   **f** b___   sp___n   n___n

Task 2 Brain cell alert! Try putting **ee** into the spaces and see what words you make!

a f___t   b___   cr___p   **d** thr___   b___n   s___n

b k___p   sl___p   w___p   **e** s___k   sw___t   st___p

c w___k   f___d   gr___n   **f** sw___p   p___l   d___p

Task 3 Croak! Read the sentences below. Tick True or False for each one, after you have circled the **oo** and **ee** sounds.

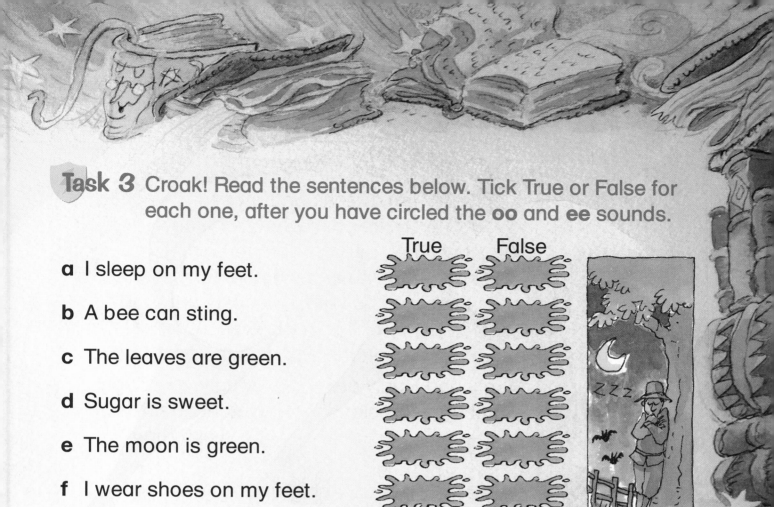

True   False

a I sleep on my feet.

b A bee can sting.

c The leaves are green.

d Sugar is sweet.

e The moon is green.

f I wear shoes on my feet.

g Fish live in a tree.

Sorcerer's Skill Check

Fill in the lily pads with either **ee** or **oo**.

a We sl⬤p in a bed.

b Apples grow on a tr⬤.

c We swim in a swimming p⬤l.

d We are going to the z⬤.

e We p⬤l apples.

f I like sw⬤ts.

g Miss Snufflebeam has thr⬤ ball⬤ns.

You are clever! You deserve another silver shield!

Terrific Tenses

Past tense and present tense are easy when you know how! They tell you whether something is happening now or whether it happened in the past. If a verb, or action word, has -ing on the end, it is in the present tense. If a verb has -ed on the end, it is the past tense.

Mugly and Bugly are watch**ing** television.

This is the present tense.

Mugly and Bugly watch**ed** television yesterday.

This is in the past tense.

Task 1 Now you have a try! Use magic **-ed** on these verbs to make these sentences past tense.

a I look ⬭ for my wand in Miss Snufflebeam's bag.

b I walk ⬭ to school.

c I talk ⬭ to you.

d I help ⬭ Wizard Whimstaff.

Task 2 Super! Now use **-ing** to make these sentences in the present tense.

a I am look ⬭ for my wand in Miss Snufflebeam's bag.

b I am walk ⬭ to school.

c I am talk ⬭ to you.

d I am help ⬭ Wizard Whimstaff.

Task 3 Now try these. You will soon get the hang of it!

a It is rain [____] today.

It rain [____] yesterday.

b Mummy and I bak [____] cakes yesterday.

Today we are bak [____] pies.

c We fish [____] in the river this morning.

We are fish [____] in the sea this afternoon.

d Pointy took us out pick [____] strawberries today.

Yesterday we pick [____] raspberries.

e Miss Snufflebeam look [____] for Pointy.

Miss Snufflebeam is look [____] for Pointy.

Sorcerer's Skill Check

Wave your wand to put **-ing** or **-ed** in the right places in these sentences:

a Pointy is look [____] for the book that he has lost.

b Pointy look [____] for the book that he lost yesterday.

c Wizard Whimstaff is wav [____] his wand.

d Wizard Whimstaff wav [____] his wand.

You are terrific at tenses! Claim your silver shield!

Rotten Reading

It is important to understand what you read. Read the story below carefully.

Today is a special day. Today is the first day of school. Peter and Susie get up early. They put on their new school uniforms. They each have new school bags to carry their school books. They each have a lunch box. In the lunch boxes they each have a sandwich, an apple, a biscuit and a drink. Peter and Susie are very excited. They run to get on the school bus. All their friends are on the bus.

Task 1 Answer these questions. Do not worry if it seems hard at first!

a Why is today a special day?

Today is the first day of ⸿⸿⸿⸿⸿⸿⸿⸿⸿ .

b When do Susie and Peter get up?

Peter and Susie get up ⸿⸿⸿⸿⸿⸿⸿⸿⸿ .

c What do they put on?

They put on their new school ⸿⸿⸿⸿⸿⸿⸿⸿⸿ .

d What do they have to put their school books in?

They each have a new school ⸿⸿⸿⸿⸿⸿⸿⸿⸿ to carry their school books.

e What do they put their lunches in?

They each have a new lunch ⸿⸿⸿⸿⸿⸿⸿⸿⸿ .

Task 2 Now answer True or False to these questions. Just do your best! Draw a magic circle around the right answer!

a Peter and Susie have new school bags. True | False

b Peter and Susie have lunch boxes. True | False

c Peter and Susie are not excited. True | False

d Peter and Susie do not have new school uniforms. True | False

e All their friends are on the school bus. True | False

Task 3 Complete these sentences. Abracadabra!

a They have new school bags to carry their school b⌐___¬ks.

b They run to get on the school b⌐___¬s.

c This is the first d⌐___¬y of school.

Sorcerer's Skill Check

Hey presto! Fill in the blanks in these sentences.

a Today is special because it is the day that school s_____s.

b What do Susie and Peter have in their lunch boxes?

They have a sandwich, an a_____e, a biscuit and a drink.

c All their friends are on the school _____.

d Susie and Peter each have new school u_____ms.

Slurp! Give yourself a silver shield, clever clogs!

Whizzy Words

Wizard Whimstaff has taught me that there are many words. Some we hardly use at all. Some we use a lot.

If you learn to read and spell the words you use a lot, it will make reading and writing much easier! Here are some common words.

I   a   he   and   is
we   was   she

Task 1 Oops! I have dropped some words that Wizard Whimstaff wants to use in a spell! Can you circle them in the sentences below?

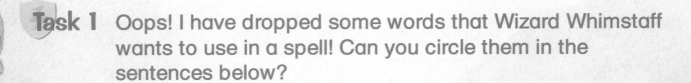

a   and   he   I   in   is   his   was

a A big dog was in the garden.

b He is wagging his tail.

c I stood and called his name.

d Mummy and I went for a walk.

e It was sunny and warm in the garden.

f Wizard Whimstaff is in his cave.

g I was happy to be in his team.

Task 2 I need to find some more words that we use a lot. Can you circle them in these sentences?

| but | it | that | to | had | said | for |

a I wanted to go, but my mother said that it was too late.

b Pointy asked me to go to the cave for tea.

c We had sandwiches and apples to eat for tea.

d I wanted to do that, but it was too dark.

e Grandad said that we could all go for a walk, but it was raining.

f I said that it is the one I want.

g Wizard Whimstaff said he would do some magic for us.

Sorcerer's Skill Check

Now put a circle round these words in the sentences below. See how many times we use them!

| all | they | on | us | it | to | said | a | he | is | his | her |

a Miss Snufflebeam is a red dragon who wears a collar with her name on it.

b They all want to be on the team.

c Daddy said he would take us to the zoo.

d Tony said he would share his sweets with all of us.

You are now a word wizard! You have earned another silver shield!

Smelly Stories

Writing stories is super fun!
Look at the pictures below —
there is a story there!

Do you know what it is?

Task 1 Look carefully at the pictures. Then circle True or False to the questions below:

a The children are at a birthday party. True False

b The postman does not bring a present. True False

c The little girl opens the present. True False

d In the box is a magic wand. True False

e The present is from Wizard Whimstaff. True False

f The little girl looks unhappy. True False

Task 2 Now we can write the story. It is easy when you know how! Just fill in the missing words below.

> Whimstaff   cake   wand   party   present

The children are at a birthday _____. There

are presents and a big birthday _____.

The postman brings a _____. The little

girl opens the present. Inside there is a beautiful magic

_____ with a star on top. The label says

the present is from Wizard _____.

Sorcerer's Skill Check

Look at the pictures again. Draw a magic circle around the correct answer to these questions. Super!

a Look at picture 1.
How many children are at the party?   3   5   7

b Look at picture 1.
How many presents are on the table?   1   2   3   4

c Look at picture 2. What does the
postman have on his head?   hat   cat   present

d Look at picture 4. What does the
little girl find in the present?   book   wand   cake

It is time for our snooze. Go and get another
silver shield!

Apprentice Wizard Challenge 2

Challenge 1 Put question marks **?** or exclamation marks **!** at the end of these sentences.

a Are you asleep

b Mind that car

c Look at the big dragon

d Where are you going

e What time is it

f It is my birthday

g Will Pointy be there

h Help I'm drowning

Challenge 2 Put the letters **ee** or **oo** into these words to complete the sentences.

a The grass is gr____n.

b The m____n shines at night.

c A b____ is black and yellow.

d We sl____p in a bed.

e You eat soup with a sp____n.

f We swim in a swimming p____l.

g I have a party ball____n.

h I like to k____p warm.

Challenge 3 Put the present tense, **-ing**, or the past tense, **-ed**, in the correct places.

a The teacher talk____ to the children.

b I am look____ for my book.

c Pointy help____ Miss Snufflebeam.

d We are talk____ to you.

e The frogs hopp____ to the river.

Challenge 4 Read this story and answer the questions.

Lisa liked bugs. She went for walks to look for bugs. One day she found a pretty ladybird with red wings. She saw a yellow butterfly. Lisa went home and drew pictures of the new bugs she had seen.

a Lisa liked b [ ] s.

b She looked for bugs when she went for w [ ] ks.

c She found a ladyb [ ] d.

d The ladybird had r [ ] d wings.

e Lisa saw a yellow b [ ] y.

f She went home and drew p [ ] s.

g The pictures were of the b [ ] s she had seen.

Challenge 5 Here are some common words we use a lot. Circle them in the sentences below.

was   his   and   said   all   in   so   they   can   the

a Tom was in his garden.

b Mugly and Bugly said they can go for a snooze now.

c We all went to pick apples but the man said his orchard was closed.

d Wizard Whimstaff was asleep, so we were all very quiet.

Put stars on the test tube to show your challenge score. Then have the final shield for your trophy!

5

4

3

2

1

Challenge Score

Answers

Pages 2–3

Task 1
a T e W
b W f I
c M g W
d T

Task 2
a Manchester, Susan, Mugly.
b London, Bugly, Peter.
c Rupert, Miss Snufflebeam.
d Pointy, Jamie.

Task 3
a The frog is hopping.
b That is Miss Snufflebeam's ball.
c We are going to the shops.
d It is time for school.
e My daddy is going to work.
f Mugly and Bugly are snoozing.
g Pointy is very clever.
h Let's go to bed.

Sorcerer's Skill Check
a <u>S</u>ari and <u>P</u>aul are going to school.
b <u>W</u>e are going to visit the seaside at <u>B</u>lackpool.
c <u>I</u> wish it was the summer holidays.

Pages 4–5

Task 1
a Mugly likes to eat cheese, but Bugly likes sweets better.
b We are going to school, so why don't you walk with us?
c I left my wand on the table, but now I can't find it.

Task 2
a It is time for Peter, Susan and Sean to go home.
b Miss Snufflebeam, Pointy and Wizard Whimstaff live in a cave.
c Where are the sandwiches, cakes and drinks?
d I like to play football, tennis and tag.

Task 3
a I wanted to say, Jimmy, that you are doing well in school.
b Listen to me, class, I want you all to come to the library.
c Are we going to the cave, Pointy, or to my house?
d What time, Jamal, do you have to be home?
e I am sorry, Miss Brown, that I am late.
f Read this book, the teacher said, then we will have a test.
g Excuse me, boys and girls, dinner is ready.

Sorcerer's Skill Check
a I wanted to play, but I had to go to Grandma's house.
b My teacher, Miss Snufflebeam, is a dragon.
c Wizard Whimstaff, are you ready to make some magic?
d John, Peter and I are going to Jamal's house.
e Put your coat on, Ann, it is time to go.

Pages 6–7

Task 1
a f d o
b m e t
c h f x, z

Task 2 bat cat dragon house

Task 3 chair dog frog hat snake tree wizard

Sorcerer's Skill Check
a e, h
b bat <u>car</u> dragon <u>football</u> horse <u>magic</u> wand

Pages 8–9

Task 1 Mugly and Bugly are two handsome green frogs.

Task 2 They worked all day to help Wizard Whimstaff.

Task 3 Then they had a long snooze.

Sorcerer's Skill Check
a John can run very fast.
b Emma likes to play football.
c We went to the zoo.

Pages 10–11

Task 1
a frog dog
b fox box
c lock rock
d king sing
e bat cat
f hay say

Task 2
a sing d hat
b fox e tag
c dog f rose

Task 3
a pig e dog
b fox f apple
c dragon g purple
d wizard h hat

Sorcerer's Skill Check
a sing ring e sat pat
b new blew f tool cool
c cat hat g bee see
d log dog h tin pin

Pages 12–13

Task 1
a man dog
b jam zoo pot yes
c bat pip ring pan
d wizard frog wand
e bee flower
f game king pin

Task 2
a pant f tip
b pan g tap
c pin h tall
d pen i tin
e pig j ten

Task 3
a sat j wet
b splat k wail
c smile l well
d slip m was
e bat n get
f bet o grow
g ball p grey
h burp q grandma
i wall

Sorcerer's Skill Check
a egg
b pin cat wand
c pat kid doll

Pages 14–15

Challenge 1
a Go to school.
b Where is Pointy?
c Can we go to the zoo?
d We will go in the summer holidays.
e Mugly and Bugly are two greedy frogs.
f The postman brought us a letter.

Challenge 2
a I would like to do magic spells, but I have lost my wand.
b It is time for Mugly, Bugly and Miss Snufflebeam to go home.
c We like to play football, tennis and skipping.
d Are we going shopping, Mummy, or are we going to Grandma's?
e Wizard Whimstaff, where is your wand?

Challenge 3
car <u>dragon</u> elf <u>fish</u> Pointy <u>wizard</u>

Challenge 4
a A beautiful princess met a frog.
b Jim likes to play football.

Challenge 5

a mat   **d** queen   **g** toy
b day   **e** ring   **h** tug
c ten   **f** fast

Challenge 6

a dog dragon fire king soup day
b pen ten leg pat

Pages 16–17

Task 1
a What time is it?
b Can you ride a bicycle?
c Where is my magic wand?
d How do I make a cake?
e When is your birthday?
f What is your name?

Task 2
a My dog Rex ate all the biscuits. He is a bad dog!
b Wizard Whimstaff turned Mugly the frog into a cat!
c We are going on holiday!

Task 3
a Look at that red dragon!
b Do you like sweets?
c When do the school holidays start?
d That house is on fire!
e Do you like to read?
f Yes, I love to read!
g Question marks and exclamation marks are fun!
h Will Wizard Whimstaff be there?

Sorcerer's Skill Check
a Are Mugly and Bugly asleep?
b Peter scored a goal!
c Watch out! Don't drop that glass!
d Is it time for tea?
e We are all going to Pointy's birthday party!

Pages 18–19

Task 1
a moon broom boot
b balloon zoo food
c cool school pool
d toot hoot loot
e moo coo too
f boo spoon noon

Task 2
a feet bee creep
b keep sleep weep
c week feed green
d three been seen
e seek sweet steep
f sweep peel deep

Task 3
a sleep feet   False
b bee   True
c green   True
d sweet   True
e moon green   False
f feet   True
g tree   False

Sorcerer's Skill Check

a sleep   **e** peel
b tree   **f** sweets
c pool   **g** three balloons
d zoo

Pages 20–21

Task 1
a looked   **b** walked
c talked   **d** helped

Task 2
a looking   **b** walking
c talking   **d** helping

Task 3
a raining, rained
b baked, baking
c fished, fishing
d picking, picked
e looked, looking

Sorcerer's Skill Check
a looking   **b** looked
c waving   **d** waved

Pages 22–23

Task 1
a school   **d** bag
b early   **e** box
c uniforms

Task 2
a True   **d** False
b True   **e** True
c False

Task 3
a books   **b** bus
c day

Sorcerer's Skill Check
a starts   **b** apple
c bus   **d** uniforms

Pages 24–25

Task 1
a A big dog was in the garden.
b He is wagging his tail.
c I stood and called his name.
d Mummy and I went for a walk.
e It was sunny and warm in the garden.
f Wizard Whimstaff is in his cave.
g I was happy to be in his team.

Task 2
a I wanted to go, but my mother said that it was too late.
b Pointy asked me to go to the cave for tea.
c We had sandwiches and apples to eat for tea.
d I wanted to do that, but it was too dark.
e Grandad said that we could all go for a walk, but it was raining.
f I said that it is the one I want.
g Wizard Whimstaff said he would do some magic for us.

Sorcerer's Skill Check

a Miss Snufflebeam is a red dragon who wears a collar with her name on it.
b They all want to be on the team.
c Daddy said he would take us to the zoo.
d Tony said he would share his sweets with all of us.

Pages 26–27

Task 1
a True   **d** True
b False   **e** True
c True   **f** False

Task 2 The children are at a birthday party. There are presents and a big birthday cake. The postman brings a present. The little girl opens the present. Inside there is a beautiful magic wand with a star on top. The label says the present is from Wizard Whimstaff.

Sorcerer's Skill Check
a 5   **b** 4
c hat   **d** wand

Pages 28–29

Challenge 1
a Are you asleep?
b Mind that car!
c Look at the big dragon!
d Where are you going?
e What time is it?
f It is my birthday!
g Will Pointy be there?
h Help I'm drowning!

Challenge 2
a green   **e** spoon
b moon   **f** pool
c bee   **g** balloon
d sleep   **h** keep

Challenge 3
a talked   **d** talking
b looking   **e** hopped
c helped

Challenge 4
a bugs   **e** butterfly
b walks   **f** pictures
c ladybird   **g** bugs
d red

Challenge 5
a Tom was in his garden.
b Mugly and Bugly said they can go for a snooze now.
c We all went to pick apples, but the man said his orchard was closed.
d Wizard Whimstaff was asleep, so we were all very quiet.

31

Wizard's Trophy of Excellence

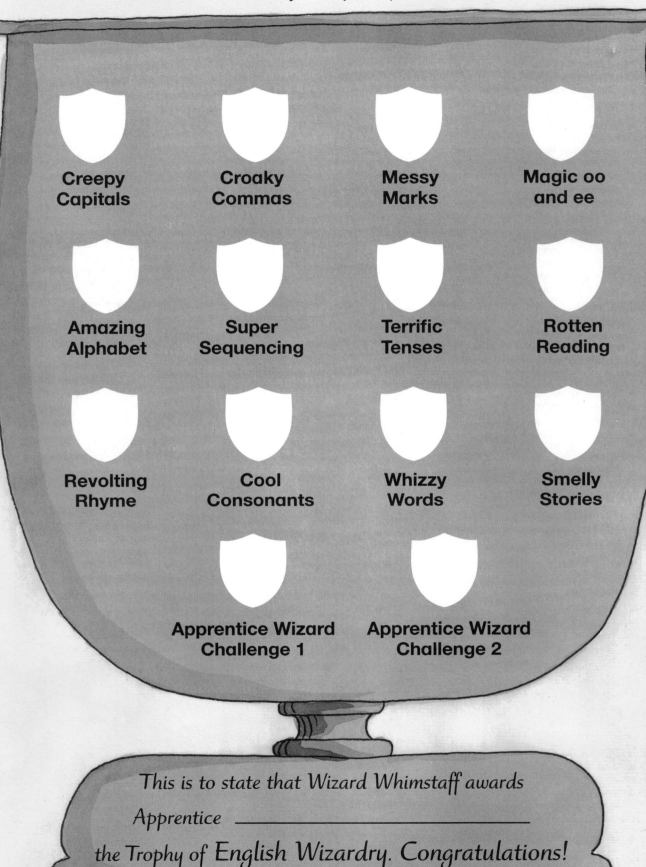

Creepy Capitals

Croaky Commas

Messy Marks

Magic oo and ee

Amazing Alphabet

Super Sequencing

Terrific Tenses

Rotten Reading

Revolting Rhyme

Cool Consonants

Whizzy Words

Smelly Stories

Apprentice Wizard Challenge 1

Apprentice Wizard Challenge 2

This is to state that Wizard Whimstaff awards

Apprentice _____

the Trophy of English Wizardry. Congratulations!